Bath is a very old city in England. It has a beautiful Abbey. A lot of people visit the city every year. And in the summer there are always a lot of tourists in the streets.

Pete and Carla are students in Bath. They like the city. Pete likes looking at the beautiful old buildings. Carla likes walking in the little streets. She often finds pretty little shops there and goes into them. Or she sits with Pete in a café and watches the tourists.

It's a Saturday in summer and a hot afternoon. There are a lot of tourists in the city today. People from many countries are going into the Abbey.

'Let's find a quiet street, away from the tourists,' Carla says.

'OK,' Pete says. He likes being with Carla.

They walk away from the Abbey.

After some time, they are in a little street behind the Abbey.

'This is pretty,' Carla says.

There are only two or three tourists in this street. The shops have small windows. Some houses have pretty little gardens.

It's quiet here, but Pete and Carla can hear music.

'Look,' Pete says. 'That man is playing a flute. Let's go and listen.'

They walk across the street and watch the man. Four or five people are listening.

'Why is he playing here?' Carla asks. 'There aren't many tourists in this street.'

'No,' Pete says. 'And there are only three or four coins in his hat.'

Pete and Carla listen to the flute player. The tune is *Greensleeves*.

'I know that tune!' Carla says.

And she puts a coin in the man's hat. Pete takes her hand.

'Let's go, Carla,' he says to her. 'Let's see the shops in the next street.'

'OK,' Carla says. They walk away.

The flute player watches them but his tune, *Greensleeves*, doesn't stop.

'He isn't a very good flute player,' Pete says. 'But it's a good tune.'

'There were only four coins in his hat,' Carla says.

'That's because he isn't very good,' Pete says. 'And he's playing in the wrong street. The tourists are near the Abbey.'

They walk to the next street.

They find a little shop there. There are some old coins and stamps in the shop window. They come from many countries.

'Let's go in here,' Carla says. 'It's an interesting little shop.'

'OK,' Pete says.

The shop is small. Pete and Carla go in, and an old man watches them. He is the shopkeeper.

'Good afternoon,' he says.

'Good afternoon,' Carla says.

'Hi,' Pete says.

'What can I do for you?' the shopkeeper says.

'Can we look at the stamps?' Pete asks.

The shopkeeper looks at them. 'OK,' he says. 'Do you collect stamps?'

'No, but I'm going to start collecting them,' Pete says. 'They're interesting.'

'Yes, they are,' the shopkeeper says.

Pete looks at some stamps from Canada and some stamps from South America.

'These are beautiful stamps,' he says.

The shopkeeper stands near Pete and watches him.

'He isn't happy,' Carla thinks. 'Why? We aren't going to steal his stamps.'

She looks at some coins.

'Are these coins very old?' Carla asks the old man.

'They're 300 years old,' says the shopkeeper. 'They're very valuable. Every coin in my shop is valuable.'

A girl is working in the shop, too. She looks at Carla. Carla smiles, but the girl doesn't smile at her.

'She isn't very friendly,' Carla thinks.

Suddenly they hear a telephone in the room behind the shop. The shopkeeper doesn't answer it for a minute. Then he looks at the girl and she looks at him. They don't speak, but Carla understands. The shopkeeper doesn't speak, but he is saying to the girl, 'Watch these students.'

'Excuse me,' he says to Carla and Pete. And he goes into the back room.

Pete is looking at the stamps. 'Come and see these, Carla,' he says. 'They're from South America. I want to start collecting them.'

But Carla doesn't like the people in this shop. They aren't very friendly, and she wants to look at the city.

'They're very expensive,' she says. 'Let's go, Pete.'

The girl watches them, and then she smiles.

'She's happy because we're going,' Carla thinks. 'But why?'

Pete and Carla go back into the big streets with the tourists. Carla is happy now because they are not in the shop.

But the sun is hot and Pete wants a drink. 'Let's go to a café near the Abbey,' he says. He wanted the stamps from South America, but he doesn't say this.

There are tables outside the café. Pete and Carla sit down. There are a lot of people in the café.

'Can we go into the Abbey next?' Carla asks. 'He wants the stamps from South America,' she thinks. 'But they're very expensive.'

'I want a drink first,' Pete says.

'OK,' Carla says, and she smiles at him.

Pete smiles at her, too.

After a minute or two they hear, 'Hey! There you are!'

Pete and Carla look up. It's the old man from the shop.

'What does he want?' Pete says.

'I don't know,' Carla says. 'But he's angry. What's wrong?'

7

The shopkeeper comes to the café. He is very angry.

'Where are my coins?' he says.

'Your coins?' Carla says. 'I don't understand.'

'They're missing!' the shopkeeper says. 'Did you steal them?'

Carla and Pete are surprised. The people at the tables near them are surprised, too. They watch the two friends and the old man.

'Steal your coins? No!' Carla says. Her face is hot and red.

'We didn't steal any coins or stamps!' Pete says. 'What are you saying?' He is angry now.

'You've got my coins!' the shopkeeper says. 'The coins are missing, and this isn't the first time. Some coins were missing last week. Some students had them, too, I think.'

'Did you see the students with the coins?' Pete says.

The old man doesn't answer.

A policeman walks down the street to the café. He watches Carla and Pete and the shopkeeper. Then he says, 'What's wrong?'

'These two students came into my shop,' the shopkeeper says. 'I went to the back room and answered the telephone. Then I went back into the shop. Some valuable coins were missing, and the two students were not in the shop.'

The policeman looks at Pete and Carla. 'What do you say?' he asks.

'Yes, we went into the shop,' Carla says. 'We wanted to look at the stamps.'

'But we didn't steal them,' Pete says. 'And we didn't take the coins.'

'Were there many people in the shop?' the policeman asks.

'No,' the shopkeeper says. 'Only these two students, and Tracy. Tracy works in my shop. She doesn't steal coins.'

'How do you know?' asks the policeman.

'I looked in her bag and pockets today,' the shopkeeper says. 'And I looked in them last week.'

'You can look in my bag,' Carla says.

'And you can look in my pockets,' Pete says.

The shopkeeper is surprised. 'Can I?' he says.

'Please look . . . please look now,' Carla says. 'We didn't steal any coins.' She gives him her bag.

The shopkeeper looks in Carla's bag and in their pockets. The people at the tables near them watch him. 'Is he going to find the coins?' they think. But he finds no coins or stamps.

'We *didn't* steal the coins,' Pete says. 'And now you know that.'

'I – I'm sorry,' the shopkeeper says. 'I was wrong. But I don't understand it. Where are the coins?'

Then the old man goes back to his shop.

'He isn't very happy,' Pete says to the policeman.

'Coins are very small,' the policeman says. 'Perhaps they're in the shop, but he can't see them.'

Some young people start to play music. A girl plays a flute.

'We didn't steal any coins,' Carla says to the policeman.

'I know,' the policeman says.

Carla listens to the music. It is *Greensleeves.*

'Where did I hear that?' she thinks. And then she remembers the flute player near the coin and stamp shop. 'He played that tune,' she remembers.

Pete is watching her face. 'What is it?' he asks her. 'What's wrong?'

'I know now!' she says. 'The missing coins – I know the answer!'

'Do you?' Pete says. 'What is it?'

'Come with me!' she says to Pete and the policeman. 'We're going to find the man with the flute!'

'Which man?' the policeman says.

'He plays in the street near the old man's shop,' Pete says.

Then Carla, Pete and the policeman run to the stamp and coin shop.

'Hey, you!' Carla says.

The flute player is going to walk away, but the policeman stops him.

'Wait!' the policeman says. 'We want to speak to you.'

The man wants to run now. 'I – I'm going home,' he says.

'No, wait,' the policeman says. He looks at Carla.

'You have the coins,' Carla says to the flute player.

'No!' the man says. He starts to run away, but the policeman stops him again.

'How did he do it?' Pete asks Carla.

'It was the girl in the shop,' Carla says. 'We looked at some stamps. Remember? And the shopkeeper was on the telephone in the room at the back.'

'But how did the flute player get the coins?' the policeman asks.

'Yes,' Pete says. 'I don't understand.'

'He was outside the window,' Carla says. 'The girl went to the window with the coins!'

'But there were people in the street,' Pete says.

'Yes, perhaps people watched her,' Carla says, 'but the coins went *into the flute player's hat!* The coins were valuable, but the people in the street didn't know that.'

'The girl and the flute player were very clever!' Pete says.

'But now they're coming with me to the police station,' the policeman says.

He takes the coins from the flute player.

After some time, a police car arrives. It takes the girl and the flute player to the police station.

'Thank you,' the shopkeeper says to Carla. 'The coins are valuable. I want to say "thank you". What can I give you?'

Carla smiles. 'Give Pete the stamps from South America,' she says. 'Then he can start his stamp-collecting today!'

Pete gives her a big smile. 'Thanks, Carla,' he says. 'I love you!'

ACTIVITIES

Before you read

1 Find these words in your dictionary. How many of these things can you see in the pictures in this book?

*Abbey   city   coin   flute   pocket   shopkeeper   stamp
tourist   tune*

2 What are these sentences in your language? Find the words in *italics* in your dictionary.

   a I *collect valuable* stamps.

   b I'm going to *speak* to that *pretty* girl. Are you *surprised*?

   c My dog was *outside* the shop, but now he's *missing*!

   d We went to the cinema *last* week, and we're going again *next* week.

   e Wait a *minute*! You can't *steal* my bag!

After you read

3 Answer these questions.

   a Why are Pete and Carla in Bath?

   b What does Pete want from the old man's shop?

   c Who steals coins from the shop? How?

4 Talk about a picture in the book. Who can you see? What are they doing? What are they saying?

Writing

5 Write about Carla, Pete and the missing coins for a newspaper.

6 What do you collect? Why? Write about it.

Answers for the Activities in this book are published in our free resource packs for teachers, the Penguin Readers Factsheets, or available on a separate sheet. Please write to your local Pearson Education office or to: Marketing Department, Penguin Longman Publishing, 5 Bentinck Street, London W1M 5RN.